Maths Mazes

My name is ....

....

I am .... years old.

I go to .... school.

I am .... at Maths!

Juliet and Charles Snape

Can you cross the swamp four times starting from 9, 7, 5 and 8 using the numbered islands?

Cross the Swamp

What's a multiple of a number?

Multiples of a number are its times table...

... the multiples of **6** are **12**, **18**, **24**, **30** and so on.

9 90 28 63 7 45 30 5 80 24 8 18

RULES: Choose 5, 7, 8 or 9, and move in the direction of the arrows.
Jump onto an island ONLY if it shows a multiple of your starting number.
Finish on the same number that you started with.
5
30
?
?
?
?
5
49
84
5
70
25
7
40
56
72
8
99
32
27
9
81
54

CATCH
Kyoto, the fisherman, takes his boat across the bay. On his way he goes between the tied-up boats catching all the fish he comes across.
START

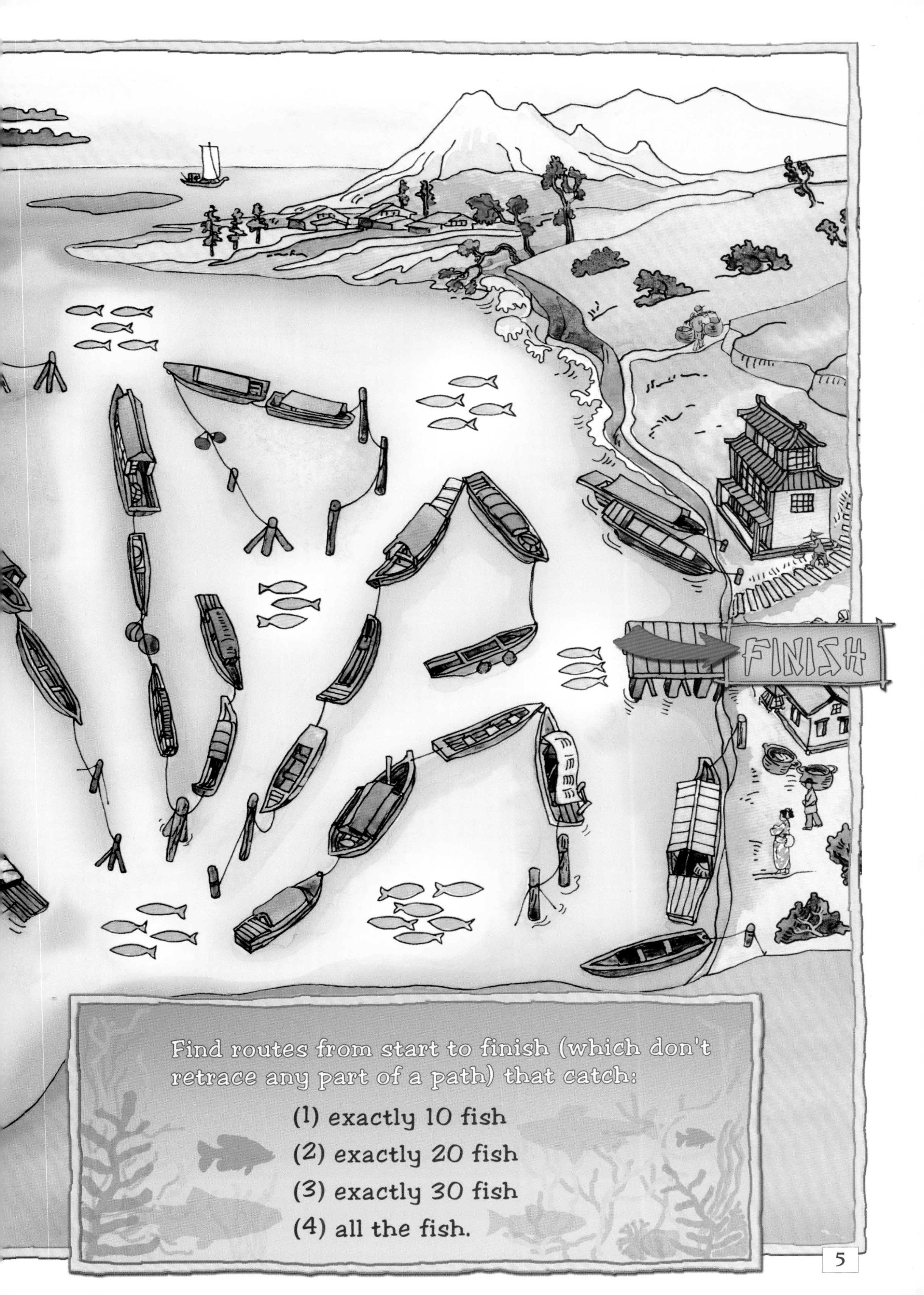

Find routes from start to finish (which don't retrace any part of a path) that catch:

(1) exactly 10 fish

(2) exactly 20 fish

(3) exactly 30 fish

(4) all the fish.

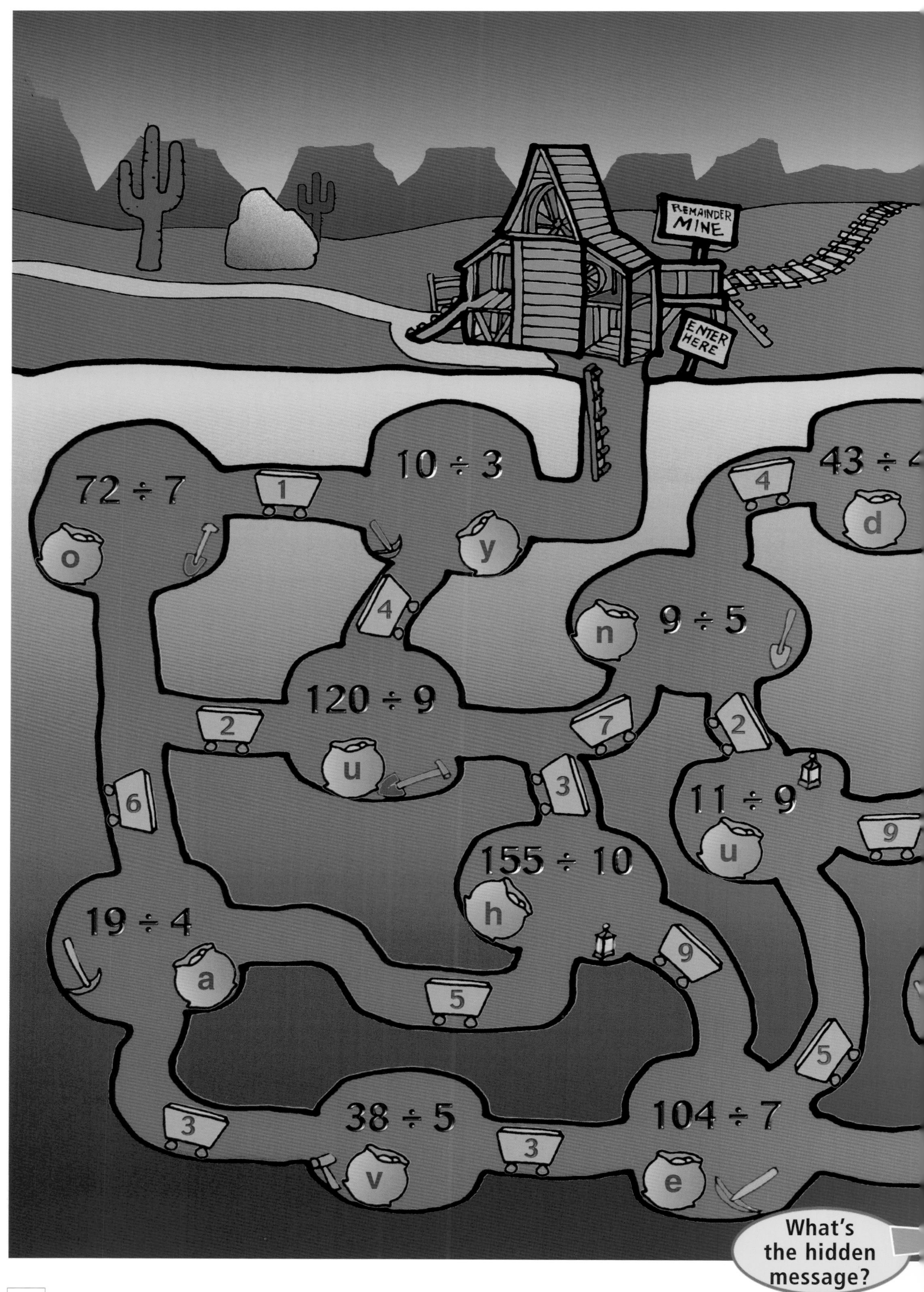
REMAINDER MINE
ENTER HERE
72 ÷ 7
o
1
10 ÷ 3
y
4
43 ÷ 4
d
4
n
9 ÷ 5
2
120 ÷ 9
u
7
2
3
6
11 ÷ 9
u
9
155 ÷ 10
h
19 ÷ 4
a
9
5
5
3
38 ÷ 5
v
3
104 ÷ 7
e
What's the hidden message?

Remainder Mine

Rules

Start at the entrance to REMAINDER MINE and do the division in the first cavern: 10 ÷ 3 = 3 r1.

Now go along the tunnel which has the wagon with the correct REMAINDER on it.

Do the next division and carry on in the same way. As you go, collect the letters from the sacks to find out the hidden message.

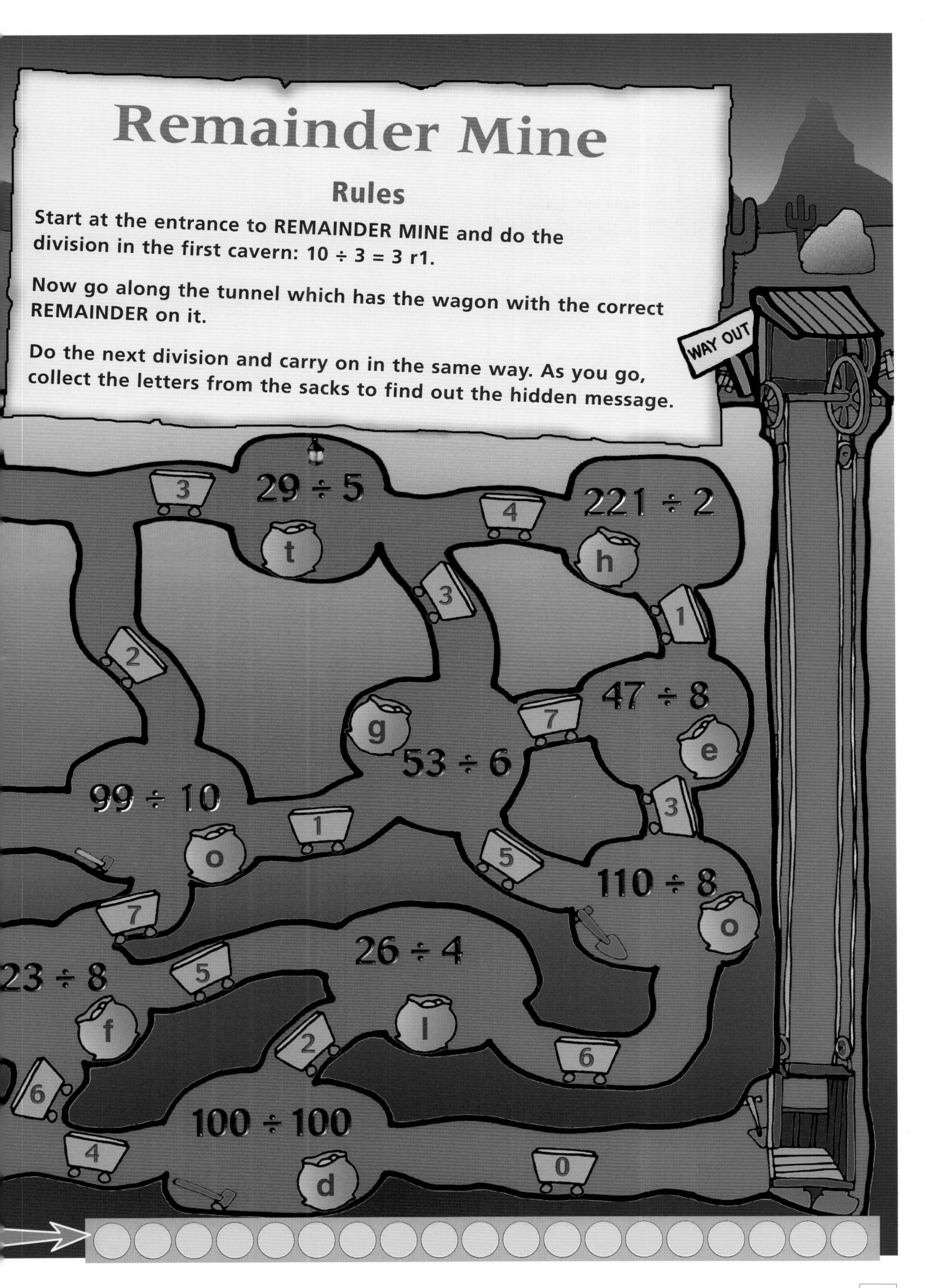

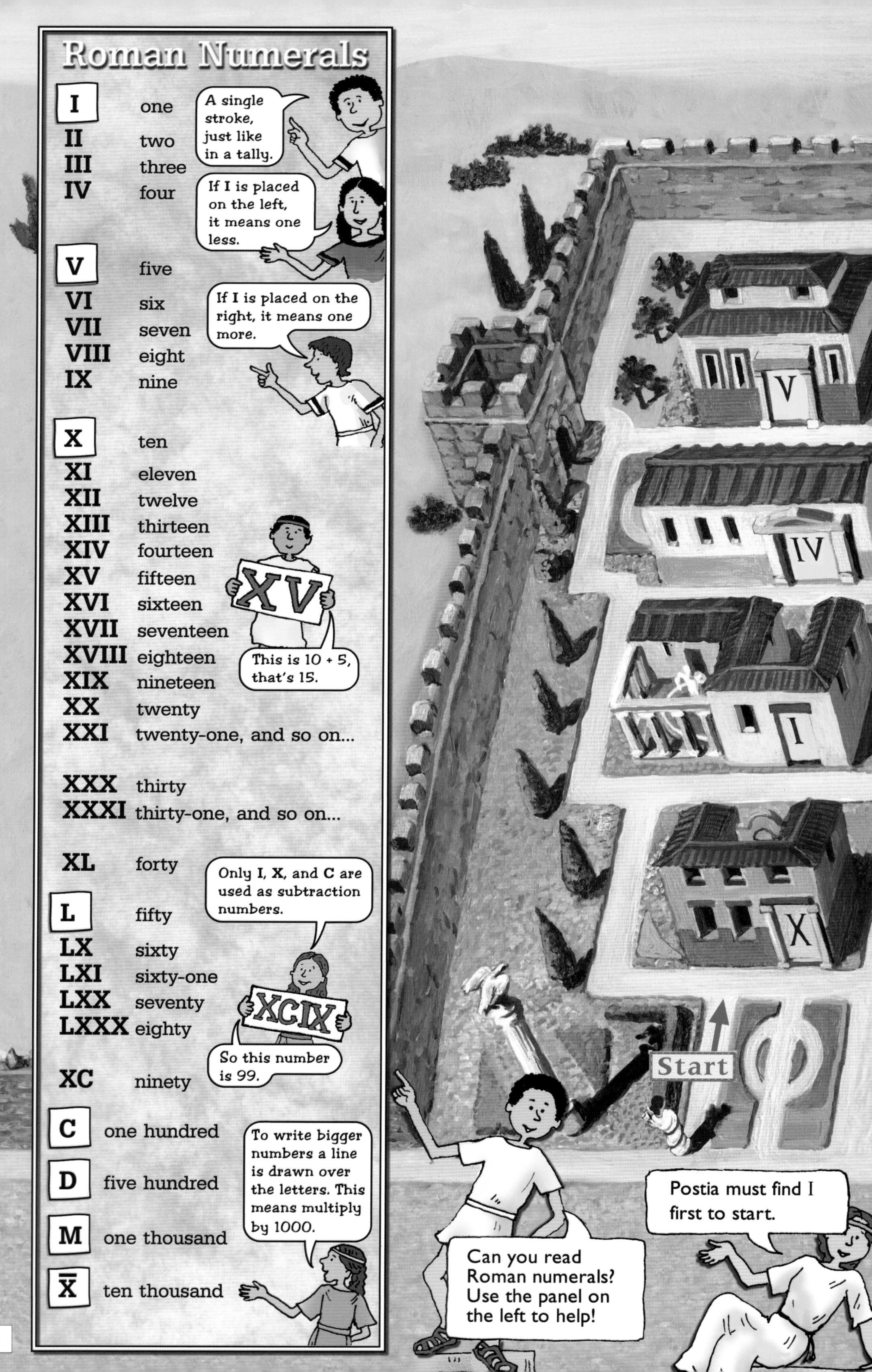
Roman Numerals
I one
II two
III three
IV four
V five
VI six
VII seven
VIII eight
IX nine
X ten
XI eleven
XII twelve
XIII thirteen
XIV fourteen
XV fifteen
XVI sixteen
XVII seventeen
XVIII eighteen
XIX nineteen
XX twenty
XXI twenty-one, and so on...
XXX thirty
XXXI thirty-one, and so on...
XL forty
L fifty
LX sixty
LXI sixty-one
LXX seventy
LXXX eighty
XC ninety
C one hundred
D five hundred
M one thousand
$\overline{X}$ ten thousand
A single stroke, just like in a tally.
If I is placed on the left, it means one less.
If I is placed on the right, it means one more.
XV
This is 10 + 5, that's 15.
Only I, X, and C are used as subtraction numbers.
XCIX
So this number is 99.
To write bigger numbers a line is drawn over the letters. This means multiply by 1000.
V
IV
I
X
Start
Postia must find I first to start.
Can you read Roman numerals? Use the panel on the left to help!

Roman Routes

The doors on the houses are numbered using Roman numerals. Postia must deliver a scroll to each of the XII houses. Can you find a route that visits each house in number order (I, II, III, IV and so on) without Postia retracing any of her path?

Omar has missed the flight on the magic carpet and wants to catch the camel train on the other side of the walled city.

Labyrinth of Lanes

To get to the exit at the bottom Omar can only go left or right if the number on a yellow circle is a multiple of 6.

Omar can only go up and down if the number on a blue circle is a multiple of 7.

If a number is neither a multiple of 6 nor 7, Omar must backtrack and find the correct path.

Can you find the way for Omar?

Multiples of a number are its times table. Below are multiples of 6 and 7 up to times fourteen. To test bigger numbers try doubling.

	6	7
1	6	7
2	12	14
3	18	21
4	24	28
5	30	35
6	36	42
7	42	49
8	48	56
9	54	63
10	60	70
11	66	77
12	72	84
13	78	91
14	84	98

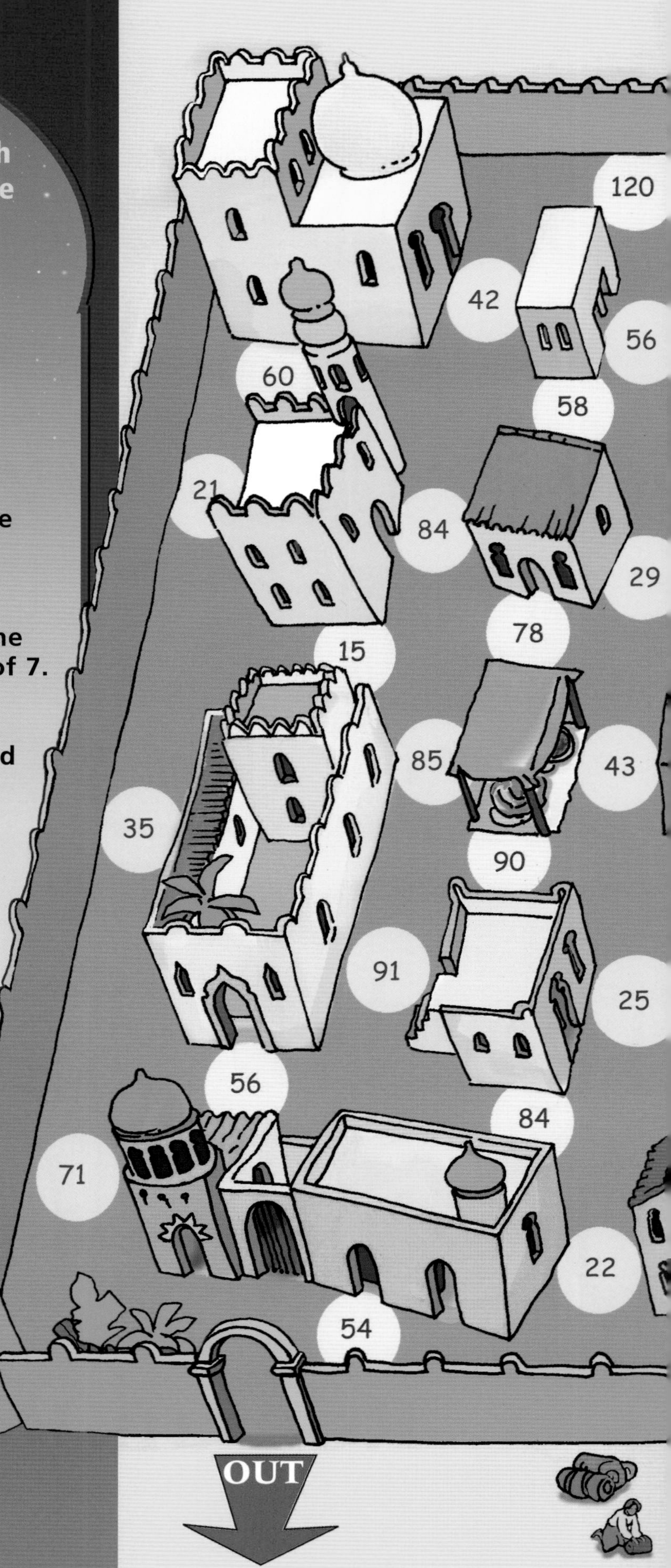

IN
108
6
12
16
14
63
42
66
43
90
140
61
37
19
19
24
34
72
49
92
28
96
36
29
32
24
50
77
30
74
114
102
76
7
70
98
48
18
126
26

Money Pit

Take £1 from here
ENTER
Pay ½ of your money.
Collect 25p
Collect 15p
Collect 22p
Collect 75p
Collect 8p
Collect 5p
Pay ¼ of your money.
Collect 3p

Can you make your way through the Money Pit? Start by collecting £1 from the treasure chest...

You must pay the demands of the trolls, but don't worry, there is money to collect in the treasure caves and from a magic lake. If you don't have the exact amount to get out you must start again at the entrance with a new £1.

How many ways can you find to get out?

Which is the quickest way?

Get to the Cheese

There is a certain rule for mice in this house. They may only go from one room to another if it has a bigger floor area. Mice **can't** go into a room that is smaller or the same size as the room they are leaving.

Miro the Mouse can smell the large piece of cheese in the kitchen. He enters the smallest room. How can he get to the cheese?

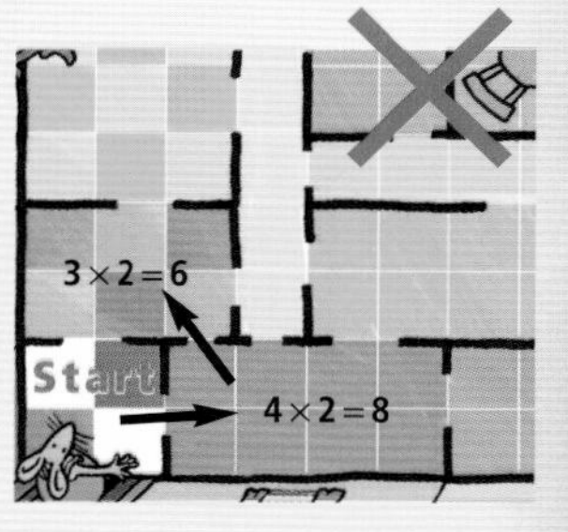

Miro can't go from a larger room to a smaller one (or a room of the same size).

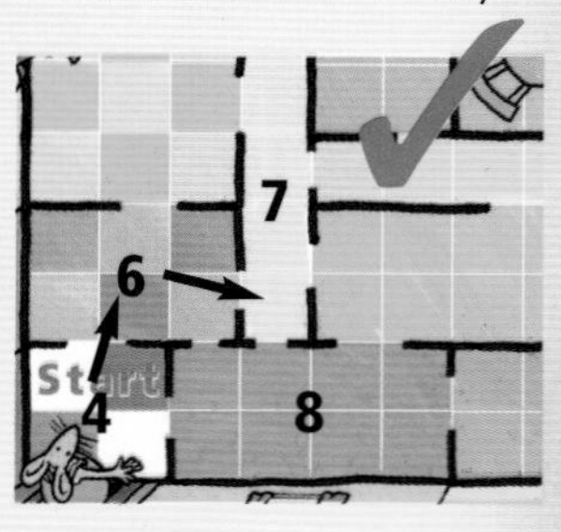

Mirror Maze

Start at a turtle in the top row and find a 'reflection' path to a turtle on the bottom row. You can move up and down or side to side, a turtle at a time. Move from turtle to turtle. The dotted lines are mirror lines to help you. Make sure that the colours on the turtle's body match the reflected turtle exactly. No diagonal moves.

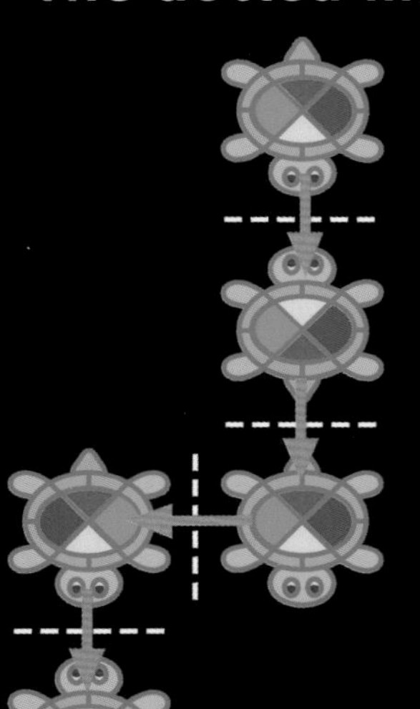

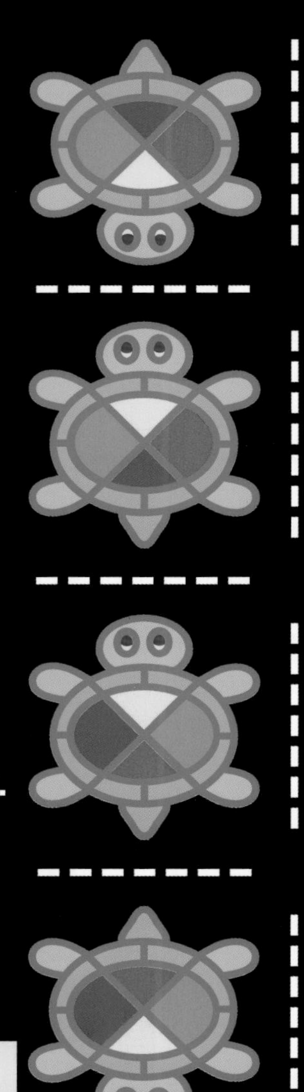

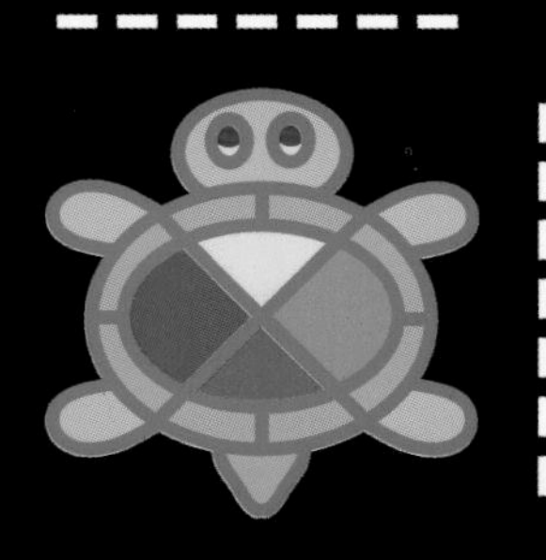

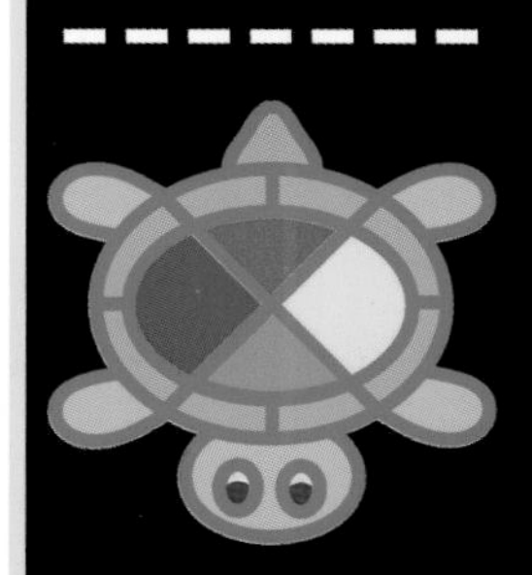

Reflections

A reflection is what you see when you look into a mirror. What is nearest to the mirror is reflected back as nearest to you.

Here's what happens when we look at the turtle in the mirror.

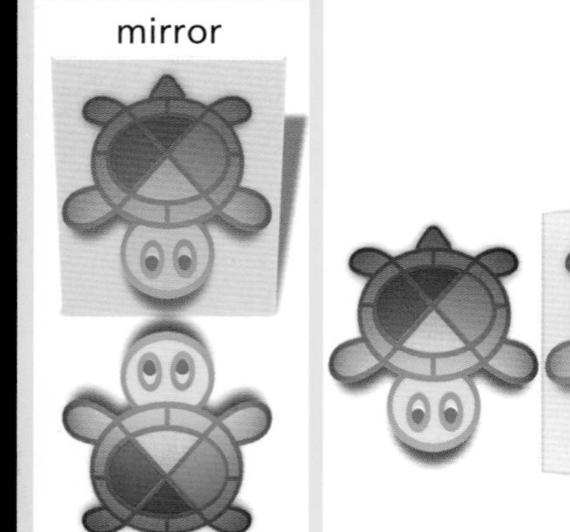

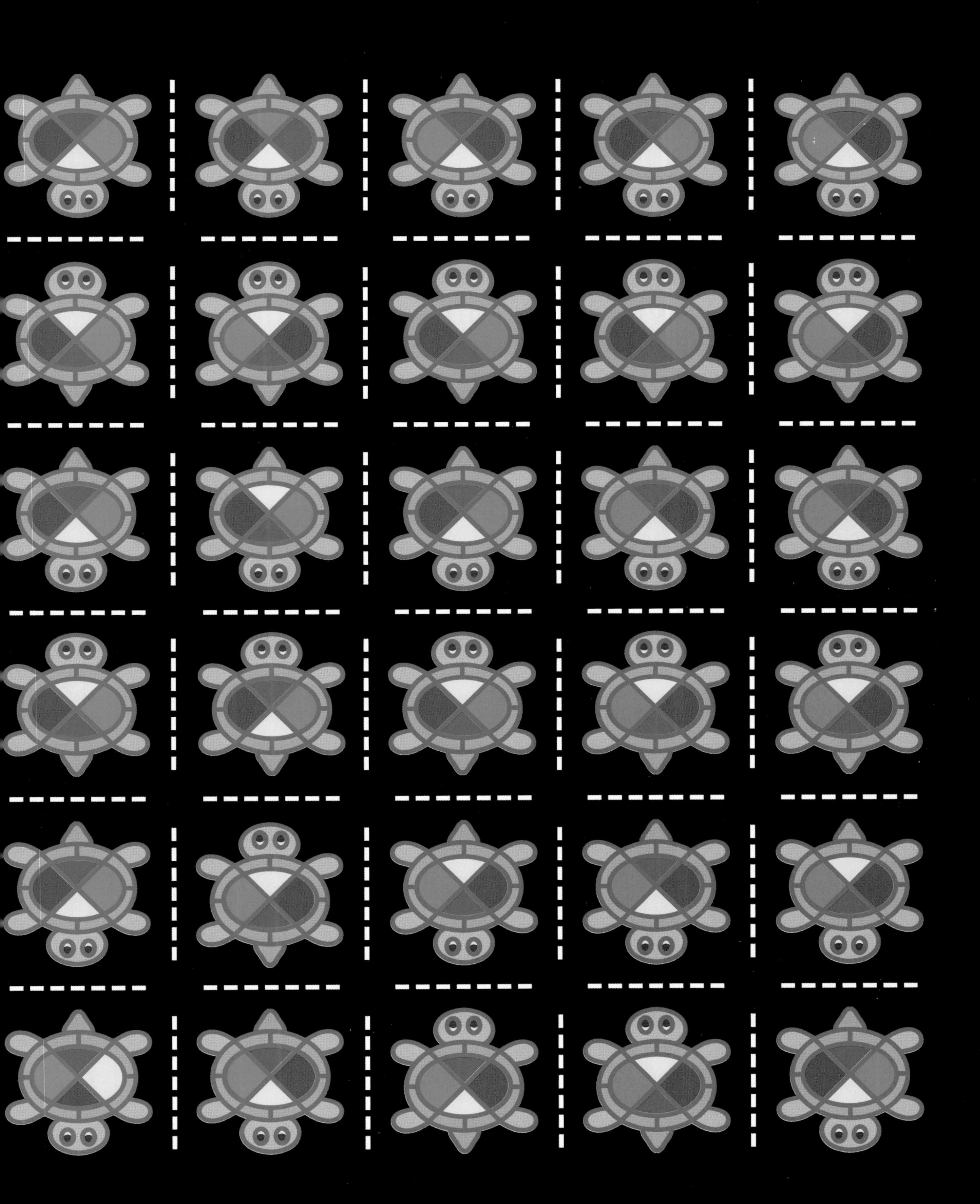

Arthur must get to the castle.
Merlin the magician has cast a magic spell over the fair land of Camelot. To break it, Arthur can only enter fields where the solution is nine.
Can you work out the way Arthur should go?
THE Mysterious Maze OF Nine
18–11
98÷7
68–59
27–18
21·5–12·5
29–20
12–3
81÷9
18–9
17–8
83–74
83–72
19–9
36÷8
15–9
1·5×6
80–71
6+2
63÷7
51–43
19–8
11–2
13–4
3×3
12–4
27÷3
5+4
2+7
28÷3

9+0
72÷8
14−5
0×9
4·5×2
10·5−1·5
13+6
15−7
0·5×18
99−91
194−185
11−3
19−10
66−59
7·5+1·5
9÷1
36÷4
54÷6
190÷19
108÷12
8·5−0·5
14·5−5·5
36−27
1000−999
20−14
45÷9
2·5+7·5
171÷19
42−33
555−546
90÷10
6·5+3·5
9−0
4·5+4·5
9×0
5·5+3·5
18÷2
40−8
119−111
1×9
100−91
201−193
8+1
3+5
81÷9
77÷8
54÷5
28−19
45÷5
2×5
65÷8

Star Path

MULTIPLES MAZE

Four starships must follow their flight paths to their base planets. They can only fly through the Star Path grid either horizontally or vertically. They cannot move diagonally.

The PURPLE starship can only fly through numbers that are multiples of 4: e.g. 4, 60, 32, ...

The BLUE starship can only fly through numbers that are multiples of 7.

The GREEN starship can only fly through numbers that are multiples of 6.

The YELLOW starship can only fly through numbers that are multiples of 3.

Can you follow their flight paths and work out which starship goes to which planet? You could use a calculator to help with larger numbers.

If you get stuck use the tables below. (You may have to add on or double for larger numbers.)

1 x 3 = 3	1 x 4 = 4	1 x 6 = 6	1 x 7 = 7
2 x 3 = 6	2 x 4 = 8	2 x 6 = 12	2 x 7 = 14
3 x 3 = 9	3 x 4 = 12	3 x 6 = 18	3 x 7 = 21
4 x 3 = 12	4 x 4 = 16	4 x 6 = 24	4 x 7 = 28
5 x 3 = 15	5 x 4 = 20	5 x 6 = 30	5 x 7 = 35
6 x 3 = 18	6 x 4 = 24	6 x 6 = 36	6 x 7 = 42
7 x 3 = 21	7 x 4 = 28	7 x 6 = 42	7 x 7 = 49
8 x 3 = 24	8 x 4 = 32	8 x 6 = 48	8 x 7 = 56
9 x 3 = 27	9 x 4 = 36	9 x 6 = 54	9 x 7 = 63
10 x 3 = 30	10 x 4 = 40	10 x 6 = 60	10 x 7 = 70
11 x 3 = 33	11 x 4 = 44	11 x 6 = 66	11 x 7 = 77
12 x 3 = 36	12 x 4 = 48	12 x 6 = 72	12 x 7 = 84
13 x 3 = 39	13 x 4 = 52	13 x 6 = 78	13 x 7 = 91
14 x 3 = 42	14 x 4 = 56	14 x 6 = 84	14 x 7 = 98
15 x 3 = 45	15 x 4 = 60	15 x 6 = 90	15 x 7 = 105
16 x 3 = 48	16 x 4 = 64	16 x 6 = 96	16 x 7 = 112
17 x 3 = 51	17 x 4 = 68	17 x 6 = 102	17 x 7 = 119
18 x 3 = 54	18 x 4 = 72	18 x 6 = 108	18 x 7 = 126
19 x 3 = 57	19 x 4 = 76	19 x 6 = 114	19 x 7 = 133
20 x 3 = 60	20 x 4 = 80	20 x 6 = 120	20 x 7 = 140

Blue starts here. Only go through squares that are multiples of 7.

Purple starts here. Only go through squares that are multiples of 4.

7	67	1
147	70	14
10	102	90
4	60	32
65	114	64
31	126	11
133	168	46
112	36	29
91	154	98
23	59	73

PLANET ZIGGUS

PLANET ZUMBOS

47	38	84	62	103	84	89
35	13	108	78	30	92	29
42	24	5	17	54	12	6
77	51	26	50	43	40	61
56	72	8	76	88	16	34
203	57	27	105	182	189	71
25	137	28	21	19	63	22
252	49	140	45	58	161	84
18	100	55	9	33	15	74
84	37	109	41	127	3	53

Green starts here. Only go through squares that are multiples of 6.

PLANET ZOM

PLANET ZARGO

Yellow starts here. Only go through squares that are multiples of 3.

Decimal Hound has six different routes to find...

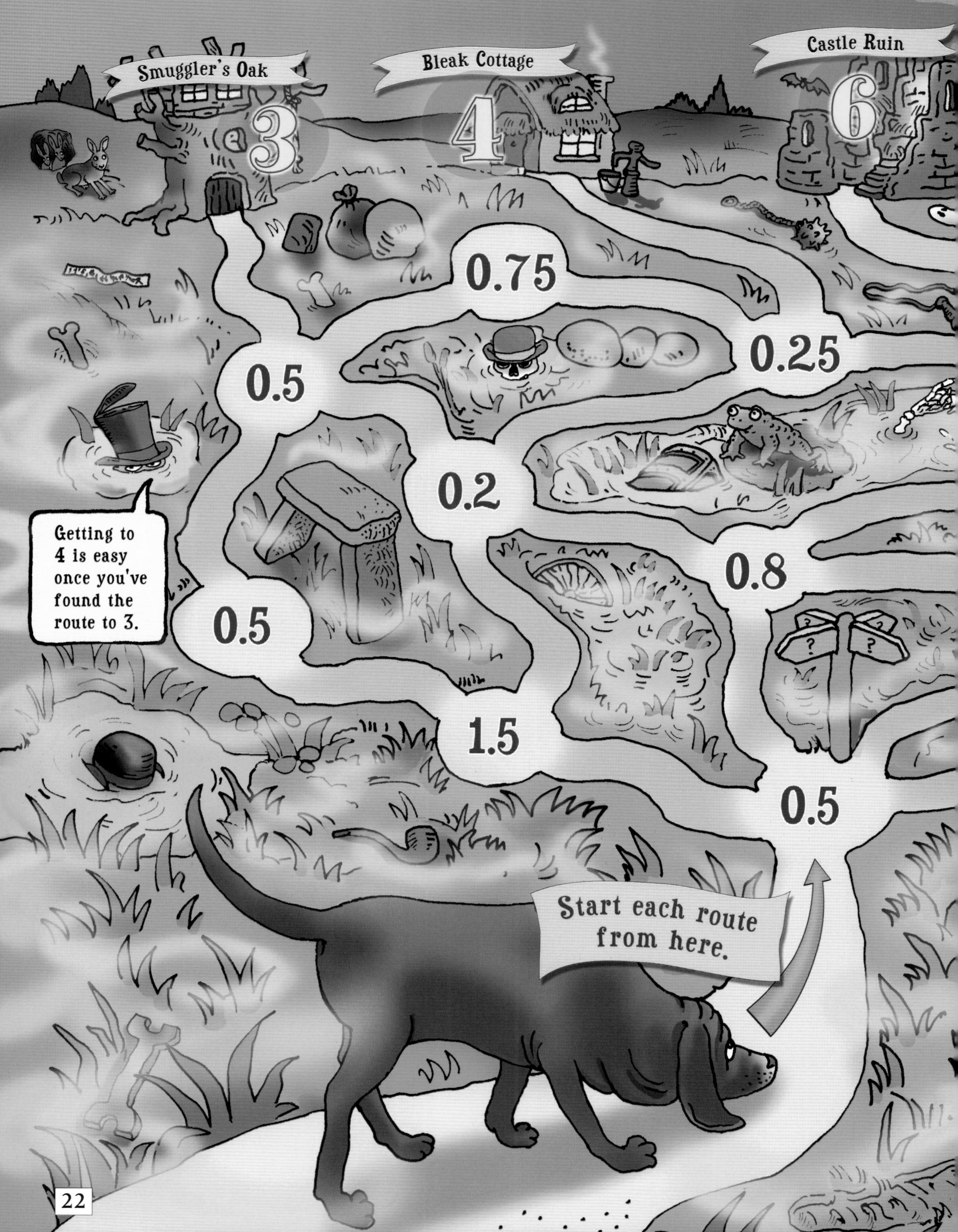

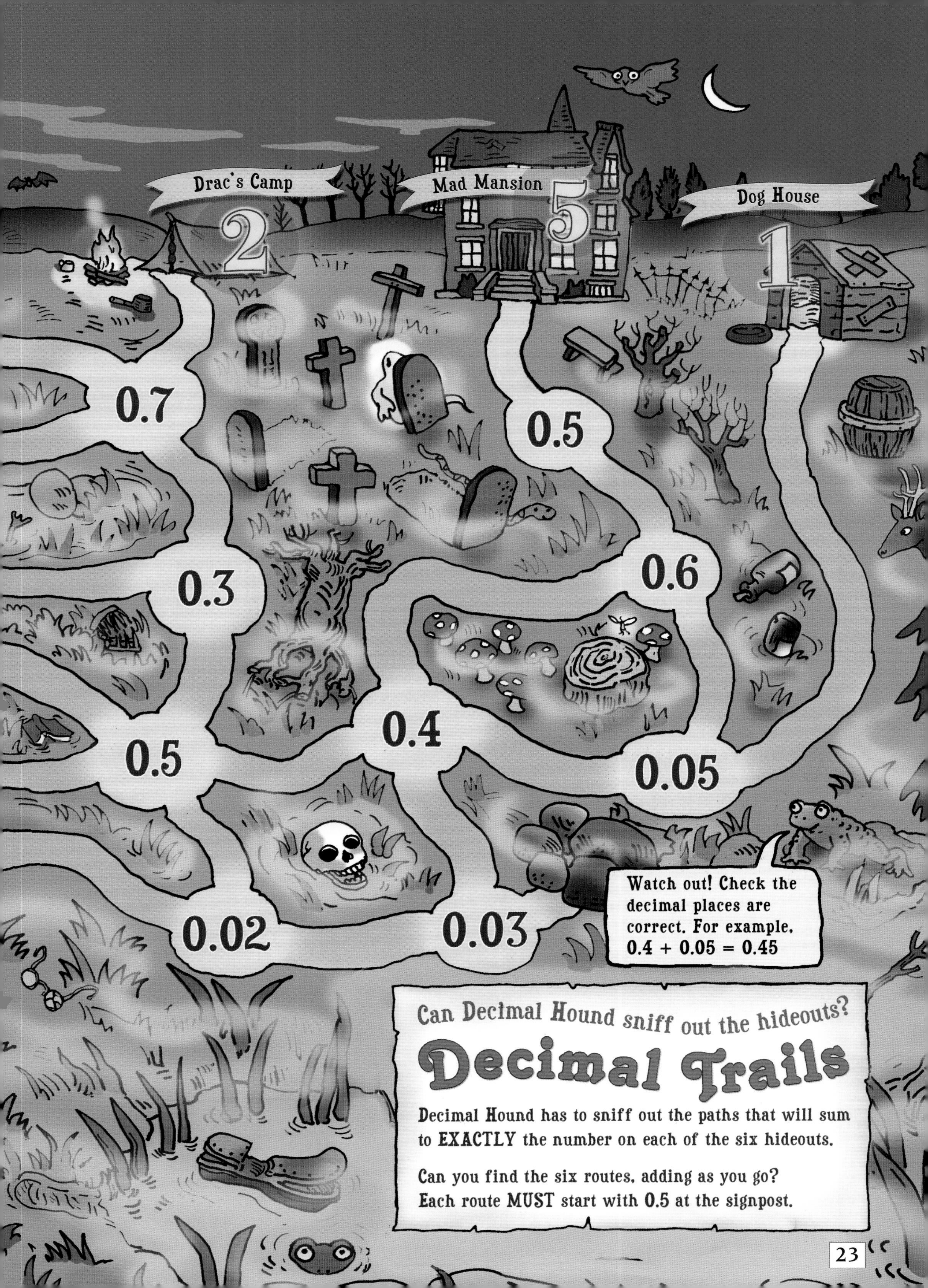

Can Decimal Hound sniff out the hideouts?

Decimal Trails

Decimal Hound has to sniff out the paths that will sum to **EXACTLY** the number on each of the six hideouts.

Can you find the six routes, adding as you go? Each route **MUST** start with 0.5 at the signpost.

Angle Castle Maze

The two knights are sleepwalking (or are they?) towards the jewel tower where all the castle's riches are kept.

Sir Thinkalot can only walk in straight lines and make right-angled (90°) turns.

Sir Thinknot can't make 90° turns. He makes acute, obtuse and reflex turns.

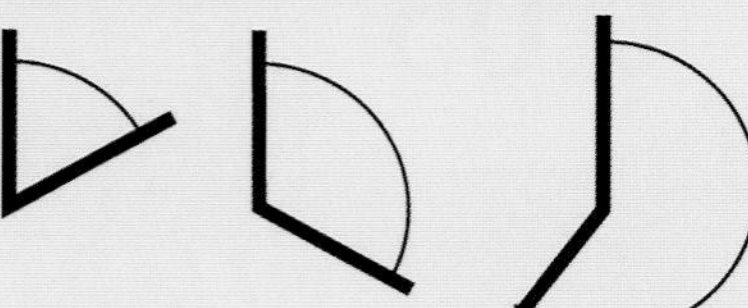

The knights must follow the coloured paths and only make their permitted turns. (They can go up and down steps.)

Can both knights get to the jewels? Who has the shorter route?

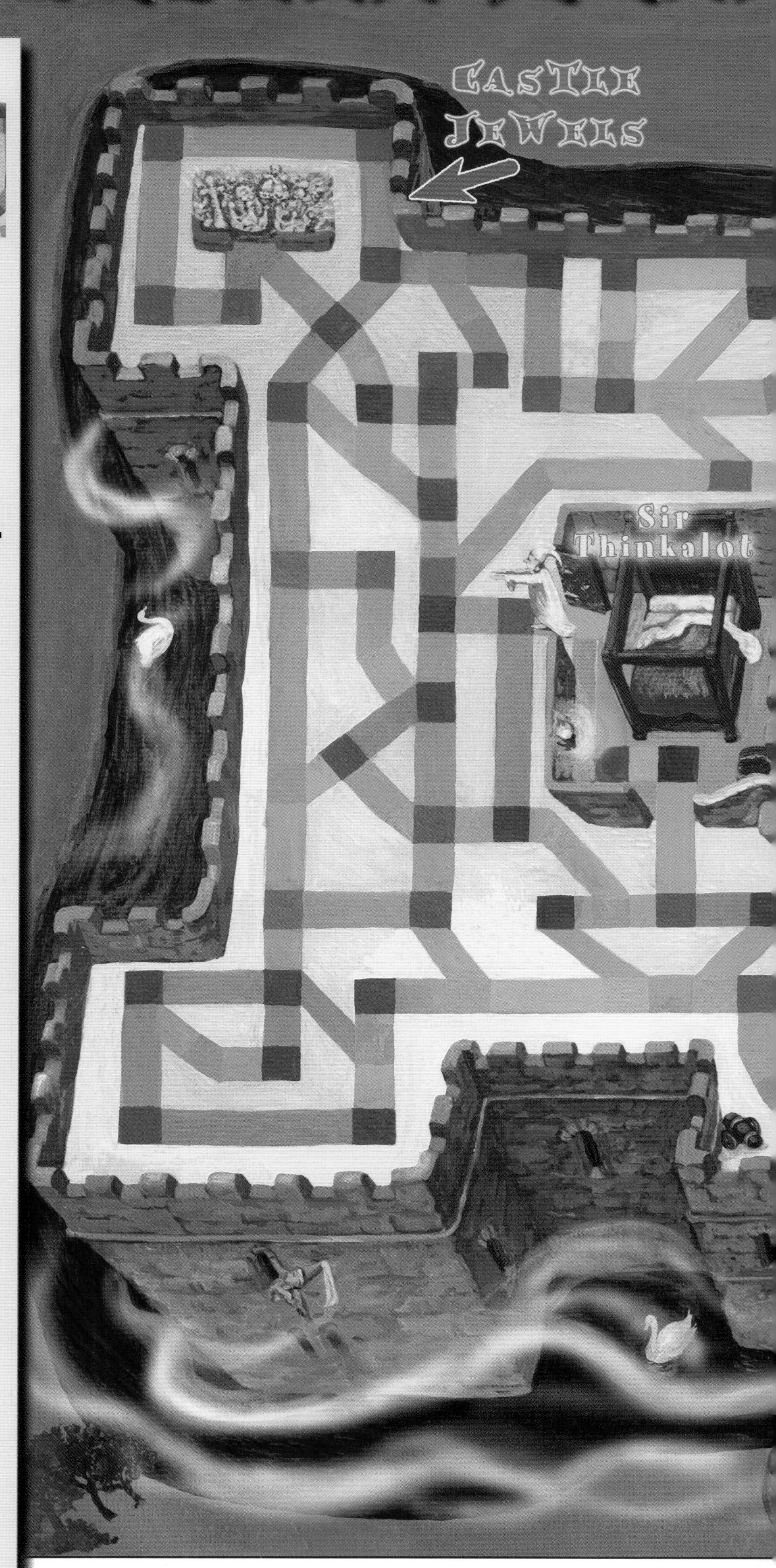

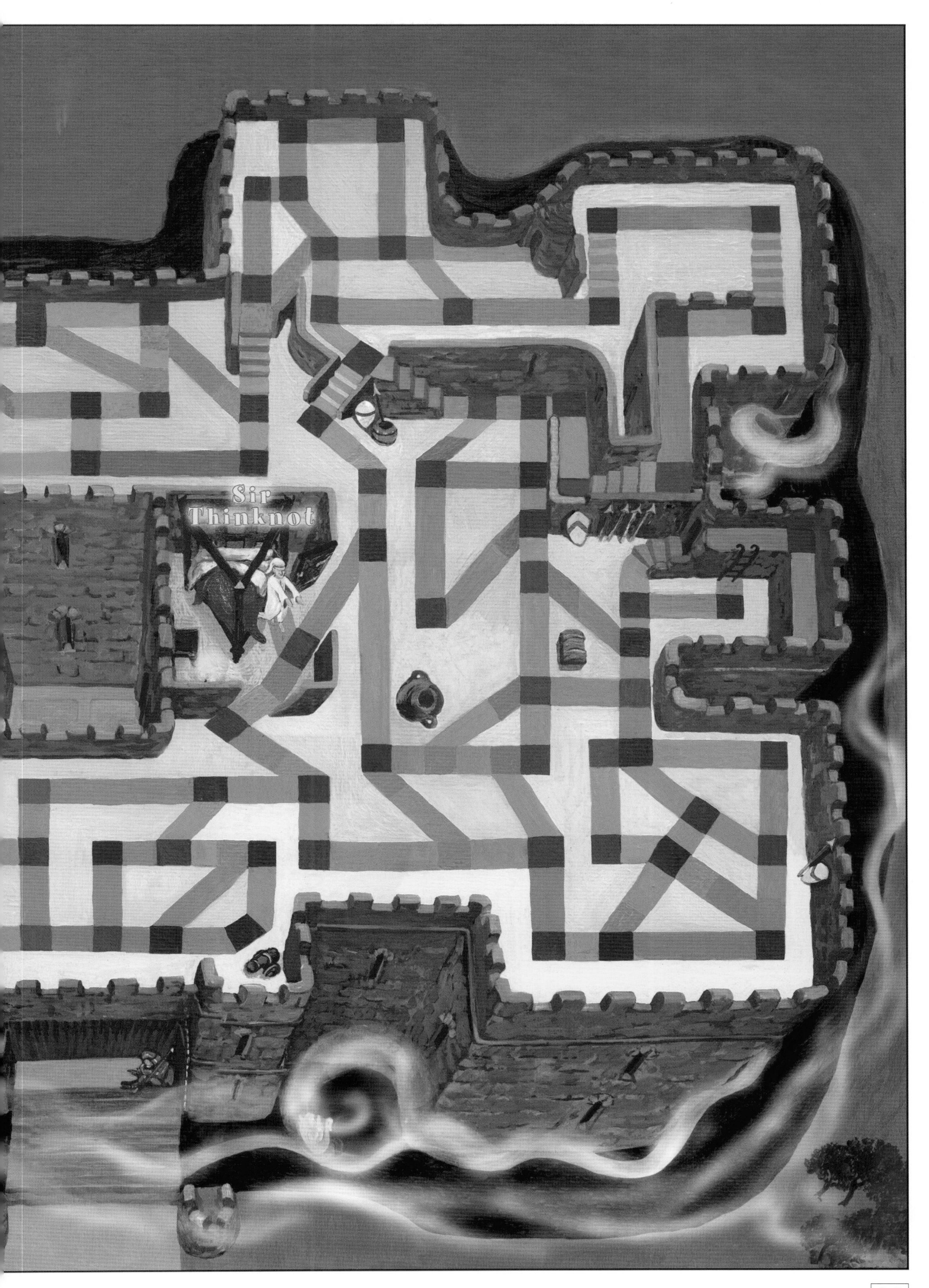
Sir
Thinknot

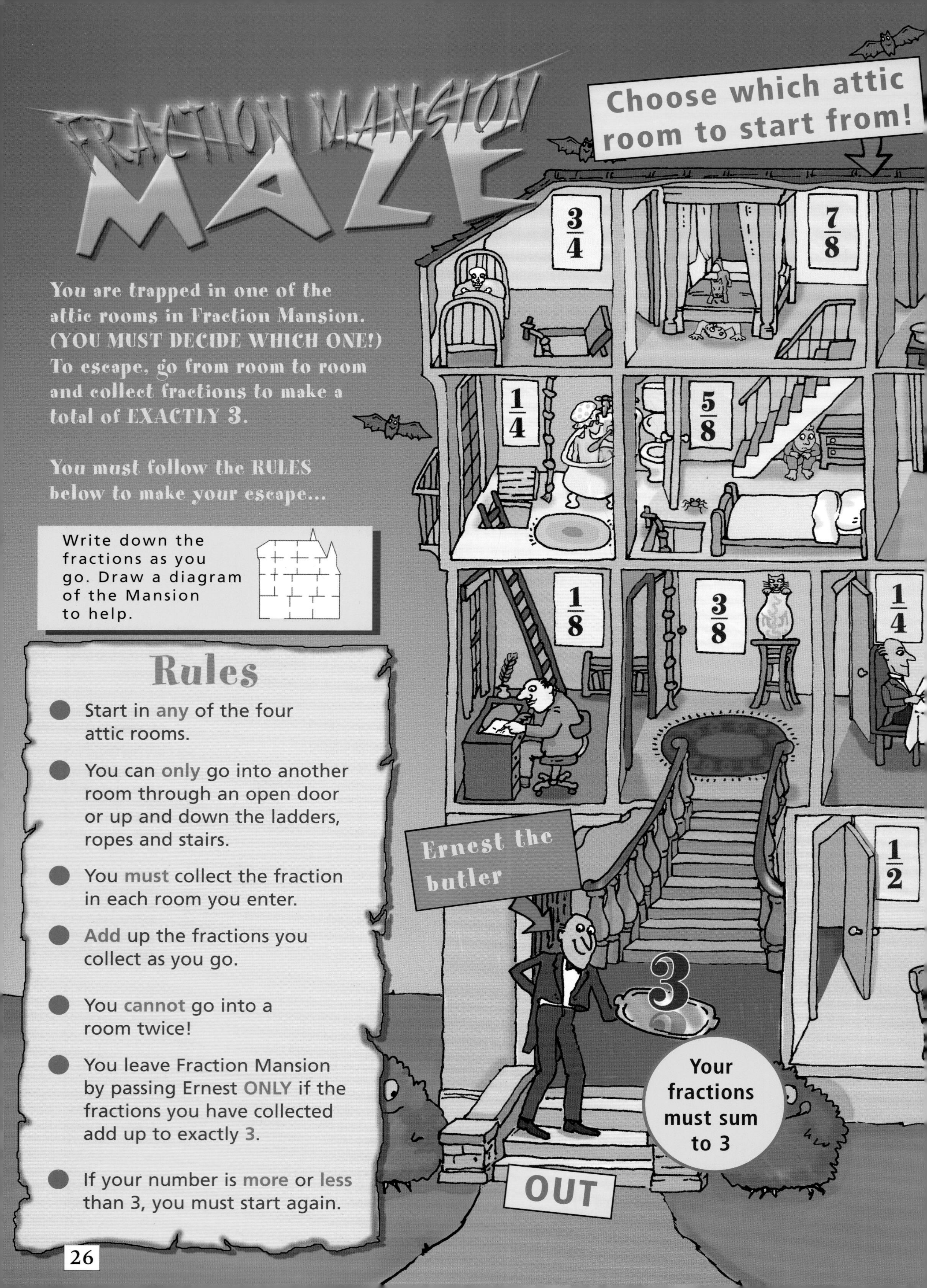
FRACTION MANSION
MAZE
Choose which attic room to start from!
You are trapped in one of the attic rooms in Fraction Mansion. (YOU MUST DECIDE WHICH ONE!) To escape, go from room to room and collect fractions to make a total of EXACTLY 3.
You must follow the RULES below to make your escape...
Write down the fractions as you go. Draw a diagram of the Mansion to help.
Rules
Start in any of the four attic rooms.
You can only go into another room through an open door or up and down the ladders, ropes and stairs.
You must collect the fraction in each room you enter.
Add up the fractions you collect as you go.
You cannot go into a room twice!
You leave Fraction Mansion by passing Ernest ONLY if the fractions you have collected add up to exactly 3.
If your number is more or less than 3, you must start again.
3/4
7/8
1/4
5/8
1/8
3/8
1/4
1/2
Ernest the butler
3
Your fractions must sum to 3
OUT

1/8
3/8
5/8
1/4
1/2
There are routes that add up to 3 from all the rooms except the bathroom, dining room and kitchen. Can you find them?

Mrs Crumble's recipe for ADDING FRACTIONS

1 To escape Fraction Mansion you will have to add up fractions as you go from room to room.

The easiest way to add fractions is to change them so that they have the same **denominator**.

2 Do this by finding the lowest multiple that both denominators divide into exactly. We call this the lowest common denominator (lcd).

2 and 3 each go into 6 exactly without any remainder.

The lcd of $\frac{1}{2}$ and $\frac{1}{3}$ is 6.

3 To add $\frac{1}{2}$ and $\frac{1}{3}$ change both the fractions to sixths (because their lcd is 6).

$\frac{1}{2}$ and $\frac{1}{3}$ become $\frac{3}{6}$ and $\frac{2}{6}$

Once they are both sixths you can easily add them together:

$\frac{3}{6} + \frac{2}{6} = \frac{5}{6}$

Equivalent fractions checker

<table>
<tr><td colspan="8">1/2</td><td colspan="8">1/2</td></tr>
<tr><td colspan="4">1/4</td><td colspan="4">1/4</td><td colspan="4">1/4</td><td colspan="4">1/4</td></tr>
<tr><td colspan="2">1/8</td><td colspan="2">1/8</td><td colspan="2">1/8</td><td colspan="2">1/8</td><td colspan="2">1/8</td><td colspan="2">1/8</td><td colspan="2">1/8</td><td colspan="2">1/8</td></tr>
<tr><td>1/16</td><td>1/16</td><td>1/16</td><td>1/16</td><td>1/16</td><td>1/16</td><td>1/16</td><td>1/16</td><td>1/16</td><td>1/16</td><td>1/16</td><td>1/16</td><td>1/16</td><td>1/16</td><td>1/16</td><td>1/16</td></tr>
</table>

You can also use this chart to work out some equivalent fractions. $\frac{4}{16}$ is equivalent to $\frac{1}{4}$.

SMALLER and SMALLER MAZE

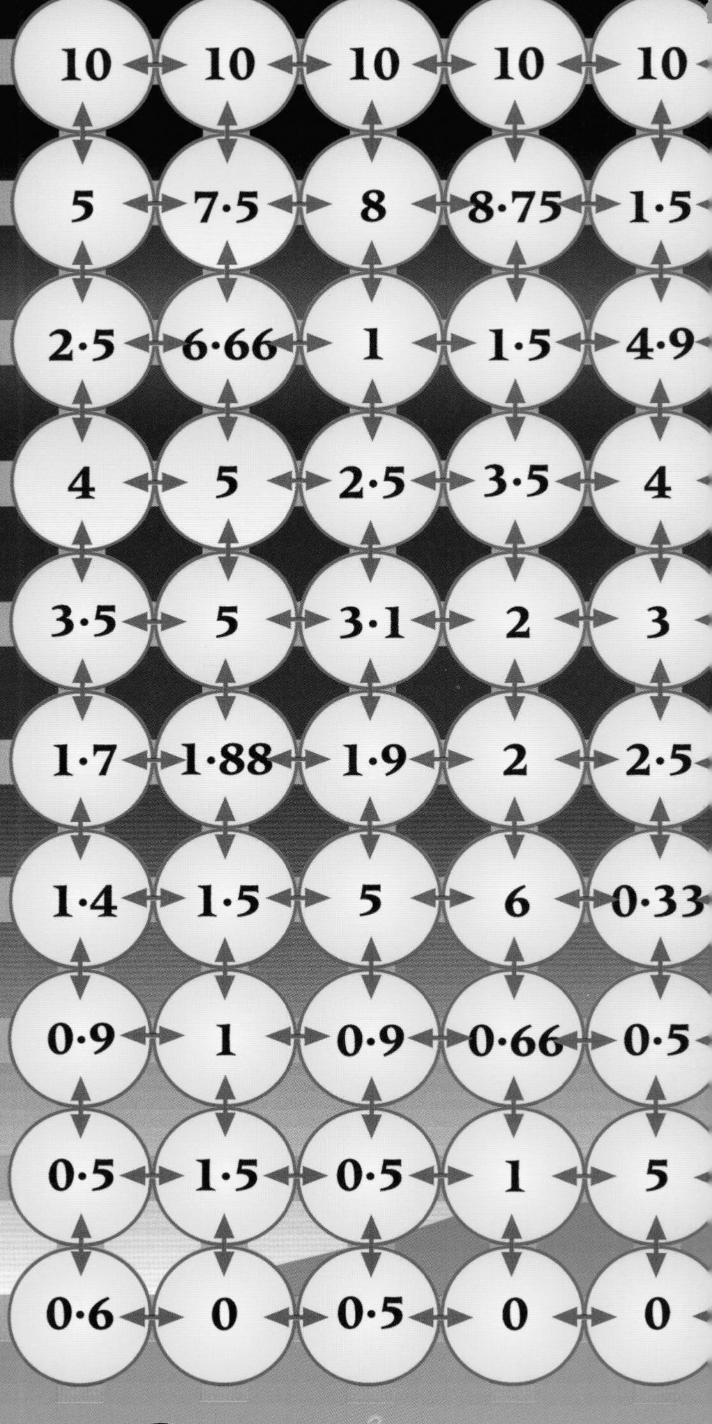

RULES

Start in any circle in the top row and find a pathway to reach any circle on the bottom row.

Each circle you move to must be a smaller number than the one you are leaving. You can't move to the same number.

You can move side to side or up and down, one circle at a time. No diagonal moves!

My number might have more digits than my friend's, but it's only a tenth as big.

10 10 10 10 10
3·3 5·5 7 5 5
5 6 6·5 6 5
3·5 5 6·4 2 1·6
3 4 0·9 1 1·5
4 0·25 0·2 0·15 0·05
0·25 0·3 4·3 4 0·05
0·4 0·33 0·2 0·03 0·03
0·2 1 2 0·01 0·01
1 0 0 0 0
My number has two digits after the decimal point.
Mine's only got one digit but it's bigger than yours.
0.33
0.4
Mine's even smaller... The first 0 stands for zero 1's; the 0 after the decimal point stands for 0 tenths; the next 0 stands for 0 hundredths; and the 1 tells you it's a thousandth.
0.001

Solutions

This is where you can check your answers, or see how to solve a maze if you've got stuck. At the end of each we tell you which part of the Maths curriculum you're practising.

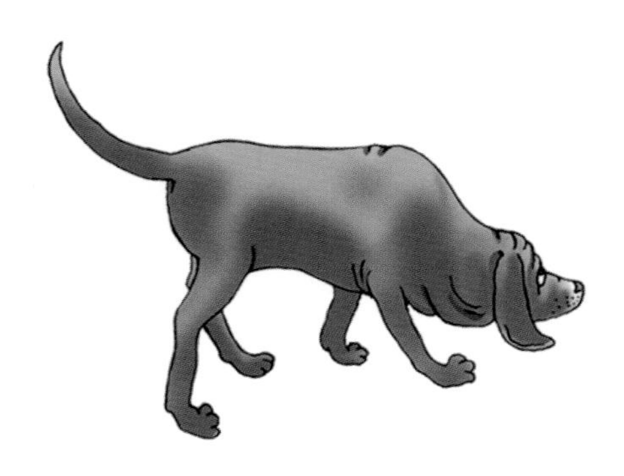

Remainder Mine (pages 6 and 7)

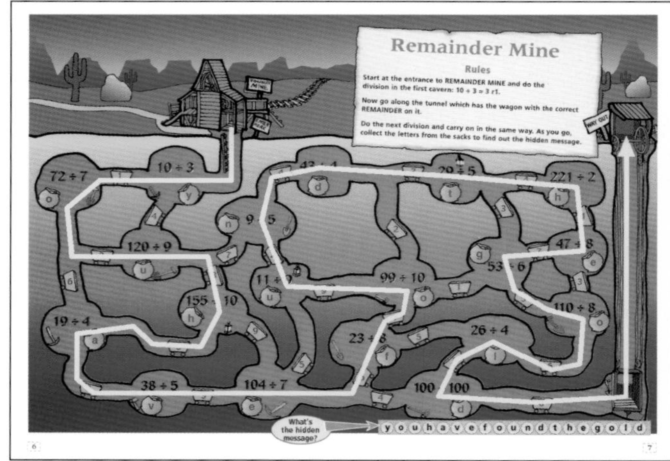

The hidden message is 'you have found the gold'.

Maths topic: Calculations, dividing

Cross the Swamp (pages 2 and 3)

Maths topic: Numbers and the number system, multiplying

Roman Routes (pages 8 and 9)

Maths topic: Numbers and the number system, reasoning

Catch (pages 4 and 5)

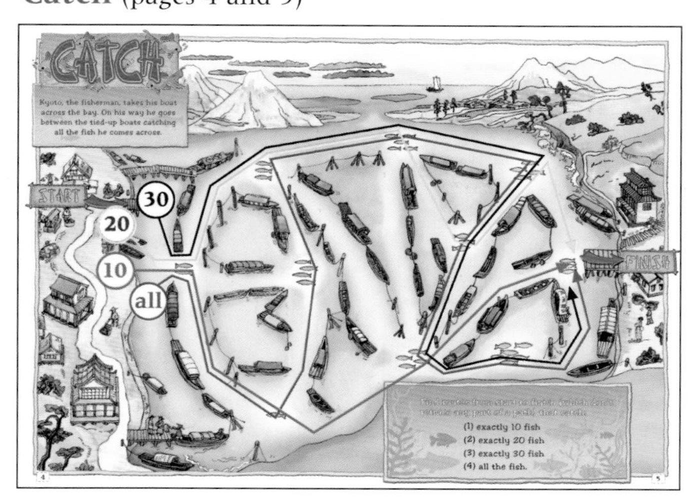

Maths topic: Calculations

Labyrinth of Lanes (pages 10 and 11)

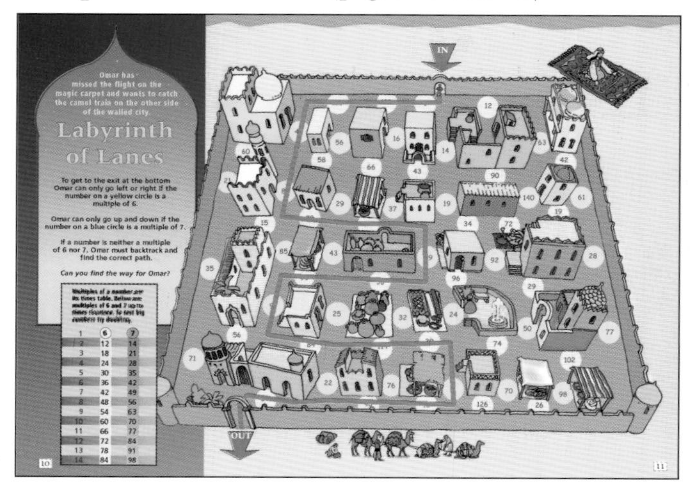

Maths topic: Numbers and the number system, multiplying

Money Pit (pages 12 and 13)

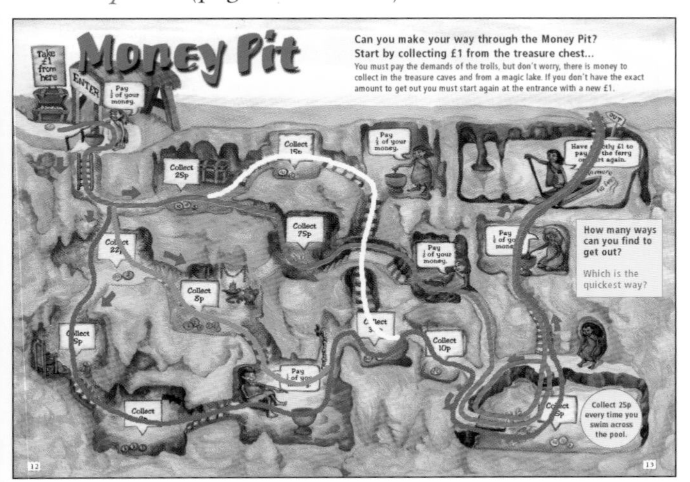

There are four different routes. The red route is the shortest but you will need to swim the pool twice.

Maths topic: Numbers and the number system, fractions

Get to the Cheese (pages 14 and 15)

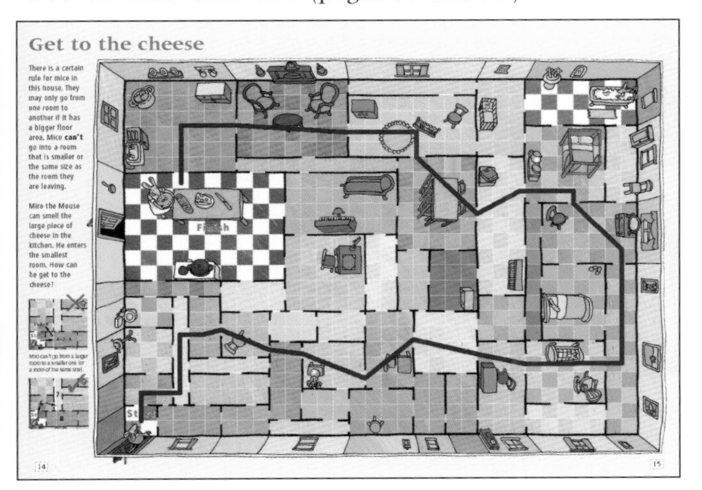

Maths topic: Measures, shape and space

Mirror Maze (pages 16 and 17)

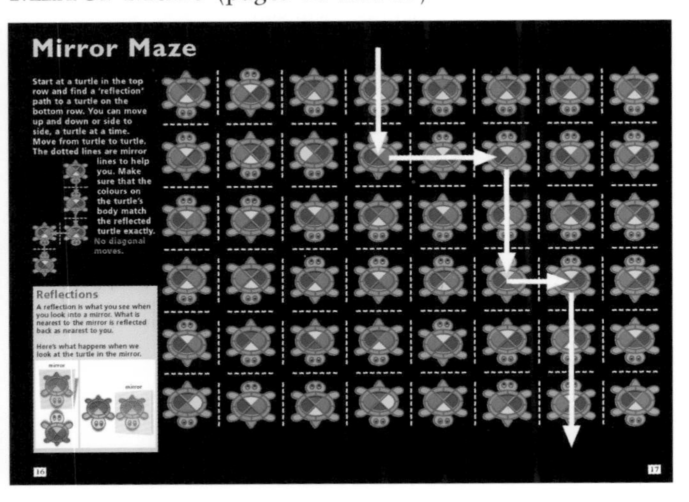

Maths topic: Measures, shape and space, symmetry

The Mysterious Maze of Nine (pages 18 and 19)

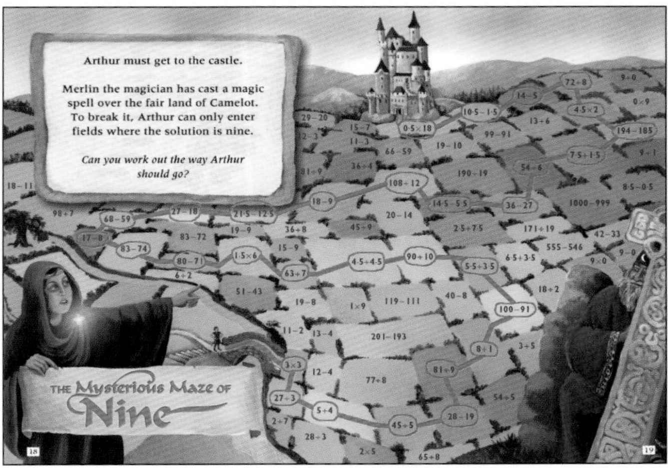

Maths topic: Calculations, decimals

Star Path Multiples Maze (pages 20 and 21)

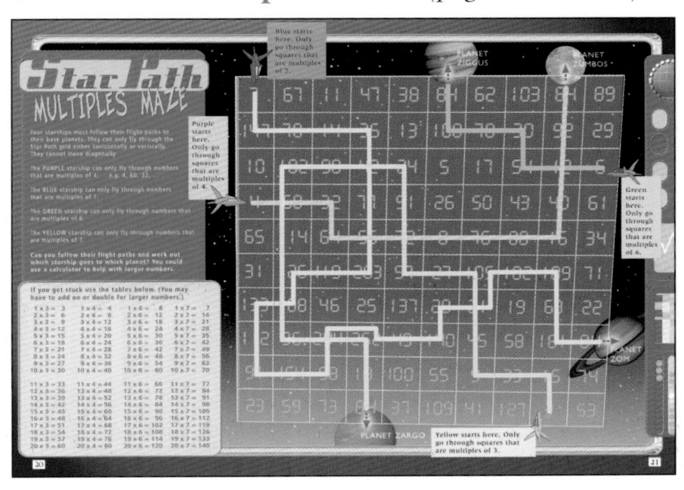

Maths topic: Numbers and the number system, multiplying

Decimal Trails (pages 22 and 23)

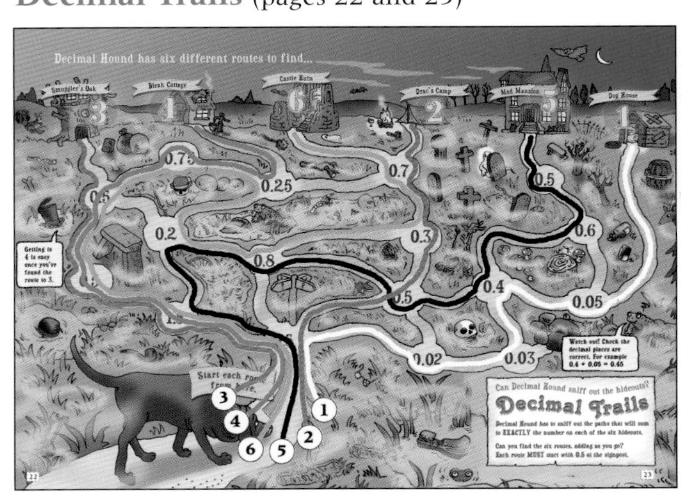

Maths topic: Numbers and the number system, decimals

Angle Castle Maze (pages 24 and 25)

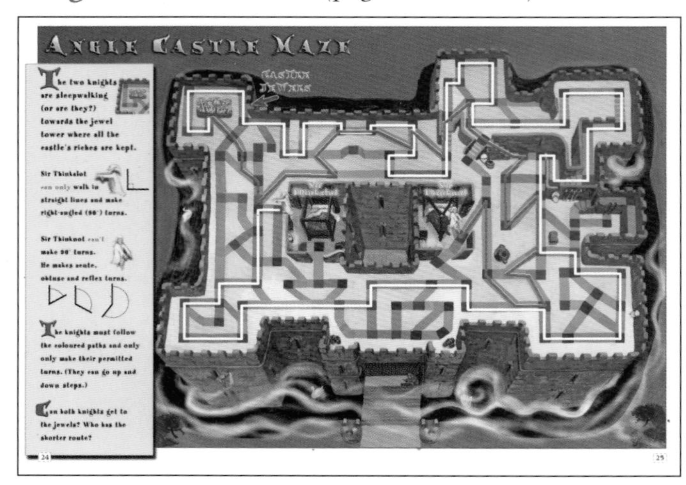

Sir Thinknot has the shorter route.

Maths topic: Measures, shape and space

Smaller and Smaller Maze (pages 28 and 29)

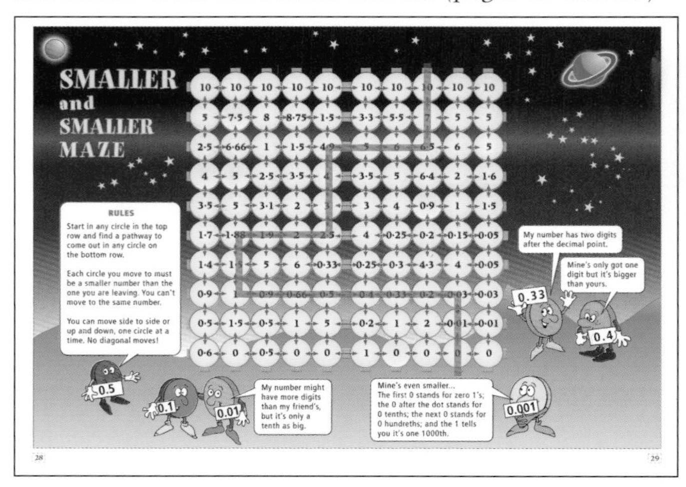

Maths topic: Numbers and the number system, decimals

Fraction Mansion Maze (pages 26 and 27)

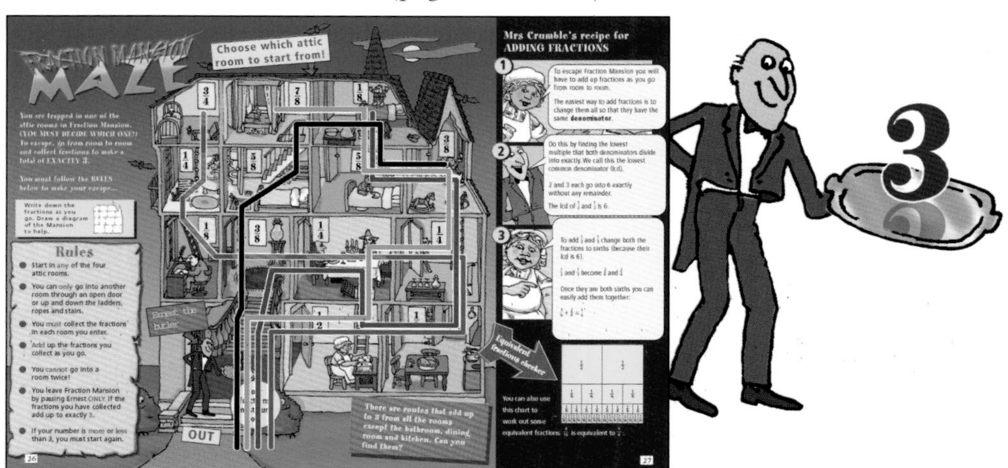

There are six other rooms you could start from and complete the journey successfully. There are two routes from the room with the man working at a desk.

Maths topic: Numbers and the number system, fractions

Published by Collins
An imprint of HarperCollins*Publishers*
77 – 85 Fulham Palace Road
Hammersmith
London
W6 8JB

Browse the complete Collins catalogue at
www.collins.co.uk

10 9 8 7 6 5 4 3 2 1

ISBN 0 00 721145 7

Juliet and Charles Snape assert their moral rights to be identified as the authors of this work

British Library Cataloguing in Publication Data
A Catalogue record for this publication is available from the British Library

Written by Juliet and Charles Snape
Consultant: Nigel Langdon MPhil, a maths consultant for the Royal Borough of Kingston upon Thames
Design, cover and illustrations by Juliet and Charles Snape
Printed and bound by Imago Thailand

Titles in this series:
Maths Explorer, Maths Mazes, Maths Mysteries, Maths Puzzles
To order any of these titles, please telephone **0870 787 1732** and quote code **256V**.